THE SOWER, MRS NOAH AND A DENTIST

THE SOWER, MRS NOAH AND A DENTIST

PLAYS, RHYMES AND PARABLES FOR CHILDREN

BRIAN MOUNTFORD

Tufton Books
Faith House
7 Tufton Street
London SW1P 3QN

ISBN 0-85191-232-X

First published in Great Britain 1998 by Tufton Books (Church Union Publications)

Printed in the UK by Indeprint Production Services, Guildford

CONTENTS

INTRODUCTION

Having published my collection of Christmas plays for children, *Stars of Wonder*, Tufton Books asked me to write some plays for various times of year other than Christmas. The result is *The Sower, Mrs Noah and a Dentist*.

The particular request was for material for Mothering Sunday and Harvest, and instinctively I turned to the parables of Jesus, many of which have a distinctively harvesty theme. I began to write in regular rhyming couplets and *The Funky Parables* gradually evolved. These can be used for public performance or for reading at home.

There are just three conventional plays in this collection: *Mrs Noah's Last Stand, Abraham and Isaac*, and *Easter Chocolate*. The style of the production is of course up to the individual producer, and will vary according to the resources available. General guidelines are given in Chapter 8. They are suitable both for use in worship and as school productions.

I have successfully produced *The Mothering Sunday Revue* as part of Sunday worship and it can be added to or abridged according to local needs.

The Sower, Mrs Noah and a Dentist is to help you have fun with children in presenting drama for worship and entertainment. It offers a finished product, but it can also be a starting point for thinking out you own production. Items such as *The Sin Bin, Some Mothers Do 'Ave 'Em* and *Brother John's Sermon* lend themselves to improvisation. However, experience has shown that to be fully effective the material in rhyme needs to keep close to the text.

1

MRS NOAH'S LAST STAND

The story of 'Noah's Flood', based on the medieval miracle play from the Chester Cycle.

Cast: God, Noah, Noah's Wife, Shem, Ham, Japheth, Shem's Wife, Ham's Wife, Japheth's Wife, Passing Man, Friend and Cat. Other children dressed as animals.

The part of God may be divided into two voices (or more) using paragraphs as the dividing point.

SCENE 1

The sound of rain and thunder. Mr and Mrs Noah, their three sons with their wives enter with umbrellas.

All — *(Sing)* 'Raindrops are falling on my head'

God — *(From on high)*
I am God who made the sun,
The heavens, the earth and planets run.
I am God who made the seas,
Zebras, lions, the birds and bees.
After that I made women and men! *(pause)*
Perhaps I ought to start again!

First time round I got it wrong,
These humans have been bad too long.
I hoped that people would be good;
Loving and generous, as they should.
But they've turned out very nasty –
Really, their behaviour is too ghastly –
Selfish, greedy, cruel, haughty;
Not nice at all, but just plain naughty.

Their wickedness makes me annoyed;
Both man and beast must be destroyed.
I'm sending rain for forty days
To flush out all their evil ways.

Everyone shall lose their life
Except for you, Noah, and your wife,
And your three sons and their three wives –
Your righteousness has saved their lives.

Noah — I thank you, Lord, with all my heart
That you should choose to take my part.
But if we're going to be saved
How d'you suggest we beat the waves?

God — Come off it, Noah. You're a rower.
You'll build a boat – a right good goer.
Make it three hundred cubits long
And fifty wide, to make it strong,
And thirty high. Then shape the roof –
Be careful that it's waterproof.
I reckon you need to build three decks;
The toilets can be unisex.
Then place the door along the side
It needs to be two elephants' wide.

Shem — And when we're ready for the rain,
We'll launch it with some dry champagne.

N's Wife — *(In a queenly manner)*
I name this ship the 'Meadowlark'.

Noah — Oh no you don't! It's 'Noah's Ark'!

God — *(Like a school teacher)*
You'll need some cabins and a galley.
Come on, *(claps hands)* be quick, don't dilly-dally!
(Exit)

All — *(A song of the producer's choice. Suggestion: 'Oh, the Lord looked down' verses 1 and 2)*

SCENE 2

(The actors retreat to the back and wings of the stage, put down their umbrellas and mime work, except for Noah who stands centre stage)

Shem — *(Coming forward to front of stage wielding an axe and speaking to audience)*
I'll wield this axe with all my strength
And cut the keel the perfect length.
Then trim the ribs and beams the same
And chop, chop, chop, we have the frame.

Ham — *(Coming forward with a plane or adze and showing it to Noah)*
I have a tool that's wondrous sharp
To shape the planks around this ark.

From stem to stern, from keel to deck,
We'll have a ship no storm can wreck.

Japheth *(Coming forward with a hammer)*
I'm an expert with a hammer
(I never was no good at grammar)
But let me have a wooden pin,
I'll take my hammer and knock it in.

N's Wife *(In a gossipy manner to audience)*
My husband is a scatterbrain.
What's a little drop of rain?
Frankly, sailing makes me sick,
And boating types get on my wick.

S's Wife Come off it, Mum. Don't be unwise.
We'll need to take on food supplies.
Raisins, sugar, flour, I think –
Everything but the kitchen sink.

J's Wife And hay and straw and stuff for cows,
Some Cheddar cheese for Minnie Mouse.
What about the lions and cheetahs
And all of the other meat-eaters?

S's Wife *(Taking up the point)*
We'll have to keep the carnivores
Quite separate from the herbivores.

H's Wife And keep the chickens and the cocks
In separate quarters from the fox,
Or else we'll see the feathers fly
Like when our parents argufy.
(They all go about their work)

Noah *(During this speech, if there is to be scenery depicting the ark it can be brought in. Noah describes the work that the others are doing)*
(Seriously)
Now, in God's name, we shall begin
To build the ark that we'll sail in –
The ship to save us all from sin,
When the rivers flood the plain.

With this trunk we'll make the mast
And use these ropes to hold it fast
When the west wind blows full blast,
Driving down the rain.

(To his wife, changing his tone)
Darling, would you like to give a quote
And state your thoughts about our boat?

N's Wife — I wonder if it'll ever float.

Shem — Oh, come on Mum, it's great – you've watched it.

N's Wife — If you ask me, your father's botched it.

Ham — Don't worry, Mum. It'll soon be ready.

N's Wife — From where I stand it looks top heavy.

Japheth — It looks OK from over here.

N's Wife — Puts me in mind of Edward Lear!
(She recites, pointing disdainfully at Noah)
'Far and few, far and few,
Are the lands where the Jumblies live;
Their heads are green, and their hands are blue,
And they went to sea in a Sieve.'
(Begins to leave the stage)

Noah — *(To audience)*
Lord, women can be crabby!

N's Wife — *(To audience)*
And men can be shabby!

Noah — *(Calling to wife)*
Dearest. I think you do exaggerate.
Can't you just co-operate?
If you keep up this silly stand
They'll think you've got the upper hand.

(N's Wife flounces off)

(To audience)
She really is a firebrand!

All — *(A song of the producer's choice. Suggestions: 'Oh, the Lord looked down' (verse 3), 'One more River', 'Lord Jesus think on me')*
(Exit all)

SCENE 3

God — So!

Noah's wife has reservations
About her hubby's limitations,
But he's not a bad old bod –
He's righteous and he walks with God.

(*Noah enters to survey the Ark. As God speaks, Noah turns to look up*)

Noah! Get ready to embark
Your family upon this ark.
And to your wooden floating zoo
Bring every animal, two by two –
Clean and unclean, birds and mammals,
Wrens and eagles, pigs and camels,
Male and female, girl and guy,
So that they can multiply.

If you're not ready in one week
You really will be up the creek,
For then to prove crime never pays
I'll send the rains for forty days,
And all the evil ever found
In town or country shall be drowned –
Washed, scoured, sluiced, submerged, baptised –
No sin at all shall be disguised.

Noah — I'm glad to be of service, Lord.
Don't worry. We'll soon be all aboard.
(Noah goes into the Ark and calls his family. Shouts)

Men and women! All hands on deck!

(All go into the Ark except for Mrs Noah)

Japheth — All hands on dcck!

H's Wife — All hands on deck!

Noah — *(To Shem)* The list of animals! It's time to check.

(Shem hands Noah the list. Children dressed as animals come on stage during the reading out of the list. Obviously, not all the animals listed will be depicted. An alternative is for children to carry large paintings of animals)

Shem — Here are lions and the leopards,
Cows and sheep (alas, no shepherds!),
Horses, oxen, pigs and mares,
Ponies, goats, and calves in pairs.

Ham — Here are camels, hart and hind,
With asses, doe, and buck behind.

Japheth — Don't forget the cats and dogs,
Otter, badger, fox and frogs?
Rabbit, hare, and kangaroo,
Reindeer, gazelle, and caribou.

N's Wife — *(Nervously)*
There's bears and wolves with great big teeth!
And creatures not to stand beneath,
Such as the Brontosaurus Rex,
And elephants of either sex.

S's Wife — I've brought hamsters, gerbils, squirrels,
Chipmunks, moles and mice and weasels.
And in this cage a pair of mink -
In forty days this ship will stink!

H's Wife — Here are turkeys, ducks and hens,
Blue tits, coal tits, thrushes, wrens;
Here are eagles, kestrels, crows,
Many more birds than you suppose.

J's Wife — *(Slowly and thoughtfully)*
If we were to leave behind
The creatures of the creepy kind –
Beetles, head lice, spiders, fleas –
Our children's children should be pleased.

Passing Man — *(Entering from stage left and crossing stage)*
If I were you I wouldn't flip
If snakes and dragons missed the ship –
Or crocodiles, black widow spiders,
Tarantulas . . . man-eating tigers.

Noah — I'm sorry, mate. It might seem odd,
But my instructions come from God.

Man — Well, please yourself, but you're insane.
I'm going home, it looks like rain.
(Exit)

All — *(May sing: 'The animals went in two by two' as young children dressed as animals are brought into the ark)*

Noah — *(To Mrs Noah)*
You ought to come aboard now, dear.

Dear? The flood will soon be here.
Don't be silly, don't be stubborn.
(Imploring)
If not for me, then for the children.

N's Wife — You're welcome to your silly trip
But have you heard the word friendship?
It's not fair to leave this town
And all my friends and mates to drown.
They've been good to me. Anyhow,
You can't just let them perish now!
If you won't stop to save their life,
You can shove off and find a new wife!

Noah — What shall I do? Why won't she come?

Shem — Leave it to me, I know my mum.
(Goes to Mrs Noah like a fawning child)
Mummy, dear, give us a break.

N's Wife — *(Crossly)*
Oh, leave it out for heaven's sake!

Ham — Shall we go and fetch her?

Noah — If necessary on a stretcher!

N's Wife — It doesn't matter whom he sends
I'm not going without my friends.

(Friend enters; possibly carrying a banner marked 'friend' and speaks to Mrs Noah)

Friend — I don't like the sound of this thunder.
Is it the end of the world, I wonder?
I'm very frightened of the water!
(Pointing to Ark)
Please let me into your transporter.
(Holds out her hands pleadingly.
Mrs Noah is dragged away by Shem)

Shem — You're coming, mother, like it or not.

N's Wife — No! No! I cannot watch my friends just rot.
(The friend runs from the stage)
(Shem and other sons force Mrs Noah into the Ark)

Noah — Welcome, wife, into our boat.

N's Wife *(Boxing him round the ears)*
Oh go boil your head, you old goat!

Noah What have I done to deserve this?

S's Wife He'd rather have a nice big kiss!

All Oh no! Yuk!

Japheth But wait! Did anyone feel that shudder?

Ham *(To Shem)*
Quickly! Go and grab the rudder.

H's Wife I think our voyage has just begun.

Noah Let's pray God's will may now be done.
(Looking out from the Ark and pointing)
O mighty and most merciful Lord,
People are mad to disobey your word!
Look how the world sinks beneath the flood.

Shem I think it's time to go below.

Japheth Clear the decks.

Noah And close the window.

All *(A song of the producer's choice. Suggestion: 'Eternal Father, strong to save')*

They all go inside and Noah closes the window of the Ark. To indicate the passing of time, music or sound effects can be played – perhaps the storm from Beethoven's 'Pastoral Symphony'. Or selected verses from Psalm 69 may be sung – 'Save me, O God, for the waters have come up to my neck.'

SCENE 4

(Noah opens the window and looks around)
Noah Now the forty days have passed
There's a better weather forecast.

N's Wife I've an idea. Why not let a raven fly
To search for any land that's dry?

J's Wife If it doesn't reappear

We'll know there is some land quite near.

(*Noah takes a raven and releases it. They all wait. After a pause...*)

Noah — It's not come back. Praise God above.
To double check I'll send a dove.
(*Noah goes into Ark to fetch a child dressed as a dove. He speaks to the dove*)
Sweet bird I trust you to return
With a twig, or leaf, or fern.
(*He releases the dove)*

S's Wife — I can't wait to get off this ship.

J's Wife — The smell below just makes me sick.

S's Wife — There's no place like home, I agree.

N's Wife — I could murder a cup of tea.

H's Wife — (*Enter the dove with olive branch*)
Look! Look! The dove has brought good news.
This olive branch should end our cruise.

Shem — It means the waters soon shall ease,
Our little bird has found some trees!

Ham — (*Looking out*)
Land ahoy! Land ahoy!

All — Hoorah! (*Excitement and shouting*)

Ham — I can see some habitat,
I think it is Mount Ararat.

Noah — Let us praise God for his grace
In sending us this sign of peace.

All — (*Sing to the tune 'Tallis' Canon', verse in unison, then as a round. Or for 'rock' version see setting by Andy Piercy & Dave Clifton – arr. Alison Berry*)
Praise God from whom all blessing flow,
Praise him all creatures here below;
Praise him above ye heavenly host,
Praise Father, Son, and Holy Ghost. Amen

God — Noah, listen to your God, Jehovah.
Seeing that the flood is over

It's time to take your wife and crew
Off this ship to pastures new.
Animals and birds that fly
Must all go forth and multiply.

Noah — Lord, thank you for your power and grace
In saving us, the human race.

N's Wife — Although I had my doubts at first
My lack of faith has been reversed.

Cat — And all the creatures in this zoo
Are waiting to say 'Thank you' too.

All Animals — (*Each make their animal noises)*

(*All kneel*)

Noah — (*Leads all in prayer*)
Lord, we offer you our sacrifice
Of thanks and praise. And give us grace
To honour you
In all we think, or speak, or do.

All — Amen.

God — Noah, I accept your sacrifice,
But here's a bit of good advice:
I made the earth for you to man it
So now you must respect the planet –
I need a sort of dragon slayer
To help me mend the ozone layer –
It takes a long time to recover.
By the way, don't kill each other!

I'll make a covenant with you
And with your children's children, too,
That while the world's still spinning round,
You'll not be punished by being drowned.

And just to show my anger's past
When the clouds are overcast
I'll bend a rainbow from the sky –
A promise that I'll keep you dry!
And so my friend, farewell, goodbye.

All — *(A song of the producer's choice. Suggestions: 'Oh, the Lord looked down', 'Now thank we all our God')*

2

ABRAHAM AND ISAAC

Cast: Four Children, Abraham, Sarah, Isaac, Scribe, Voice, Two Gossips, Boy, Girl, Two Servants, Rebekah.

SCENE 1

Abraham is in bed sleeping. While he sleeps he dreams. The actors enter and gather round him in an arc.

All — *(Whisper – softly and getting louder)*
Abraham, Abraham.
Abraham, Abraham.

Child 1 — Could you really have done it, Abraham?

(Pause)

Child 2 — Could you really have killed your son?

(Pause)

Child 3 — Is God that important to you, Abraham?

(Pause)

Child 1 — Remember Mount Moriah.

Child 2 — Remember the fire.

Child 3 — Remember the knife.

Child 4 — Remember Isaac in fear for his life.

(Pause)

Sarah — See that he comes to no harm, Abraham.

Isaac — But the knife, Father. It frightens me.

Child 4 — What kind of God demands the life of your son?

Abraham — *(Waking, cries out)* No. No.

Child 1 — Could you really have done it, Abraham?

Child 3 — Is God that important to you?

Abraham — *(Shouting)* Stop!

(Music. Exit all except Abraham and Sarah)

SCENE 2

A Scribe is seated at his desk writing with a reed pen on papyrus

Scribe — Abraham often had nightmares like this – ever since the dreadful events I am going to tell you about.

Abraham and Sarah longed to have children, but had none of their own. One day Abraham was sitting under his favourite oak tree keeping out of the sun, when he had a strange feeling that he was not alone. Then he thought he heard a voice speaking to him.

Voice — *(From on high)*
Abraham! This is the Lord your God.
I have decided to bless you and your wife, Sarah.
I am going to give you both a son!

Abraham — *(Roars with laughter)* Lord, is this some sort of joke? Look at us – we're old people. I'm a hundred years old, and Sarah was ninety last birthday.

Voice — Don't be such a wimp, Abraham. To me all things are possible. But first, can we shake hands on something? The deal is this: you and your people must be faithful to me, and in return I will give you the Land of Canaan as your own country. Just keep my commandments and you will have as many children as there are stars in the sky.

(Exit Abraham)

Scribe — It was true. Sarah found that she was going to have a baby, and when the news got out people couldn't believe it.

(Enter two gossips)

Gossip 1 — You'll never guess what I heard this morning.

Gossip 2 — No, go on tell me. I love gossip.

Gossip 1 — *(Using hands to indicate pregnancy)* Old Sarah – Abraham's wife – is, you know...

Gossip 2 — *(Gasps)* No. I don't believe it.

Gossip 1 — *(Nodding)* Yes.

Gossip 2 — What? Pregnant?
(They both giggle. Exit)

Scribe — Sarah was so pleased she didn't know whether to laugh or cry. She said to herself:

Sarah — 'God has brought laughter for me; everyone who hears will laugh with me.' *(Exit)*

SCENE 3
(Enter Abraham)

Scribe — When Isaac was born Abraham
Frisked and frolicked like a lamb.
He bounced about and jumped for joy.

Abraham — Hey! Listen folks. I've got a boy. *(Pause)*
How're we going to celebrate?
I know! We'll dance from six 'til late.
(Thinks for a moment)
Because this is my special son,
The party is for everyone.
We'll have a band and loads to eat
And set up tables in the street.

(Enter All. Music and dancing. The producer can choose between disco music and free style dancing or a choreographed dance to the song that follows)

Dance, dance, and praise the Lord,
A babe is born, a babe is born.
Dance, dance and praise the Lord,
A babe is born to Sarah.

Abraham gives thanks to God;
A babe is born, a babe is born.
Araham gives thanks to God;
A babe is born to Sarah.

Sarah sings joyfully;
A babe is born, a babe is born.
Sarah sings joyfully;
A babe is born to Sarah.

(The girls congratulate Sarah, who is holding the baby. Some kiss her. The boys shake Abraham by the hand)

Girl — Congratulations, Sarah. God has given you a beautiful child.

Boy — Well done, Abraham.

(All chatter creating a party hubbub)

Abraham — *(Bangs a spoon on the table to call everyone to order)* Quiet everybody. *(Pause)* Can we have a bit of hush, please? Thank you. I won't keep you a moment.

My friends, thank you all for coming here today. It's a wonderful day for Sarah and me – a day that we never dreamed would happen. So please will you all raise your glasses and drink a toast to Isaac.

All — Isaac. Long life and happiness.

Abraham — Isaac's birth is a sign of God's love for us all.

Child 2 — Hear, hear. Well said Abraham.

Abraham — And I want to make a very special promise in front of you all today – a very special promise. Because he has given us a child of our own, from now on I will do whatever God asks of me.

Boy — Three cheers for Abraham. Hip, hip, hip …

All — Hooray.

Boy — Hip, hip, hip …

All — Hooray.

Boy — Hip, hip, hip …

All — Hooray.

(All exit singing, 'Dance, dance, and praise the Lord' or to disco music)

SCENE 4

Scribe — When I was a kid my mother used to call me 'Tiddles'. Very embarrassing when my friends came round! 'Tiddles is hoping to be a scribe,' she'd say, 'aren't you Tiddles?' And they'd all go, 'Miaow' and smooth out imaginary whiskers as if they were cats. Sarah's pet name for Isaac was 'Sicky', so his friends called him 'Yuk'. She had called him 'Sicky' when he was a baby and couldn't get out of the habit because she thought he was so sweet.

His mum and dad thought he was the most wonderful boy in the world and had great things in mind for him when he grew up. But then one day God spoke to Abraham and these high hopes were suddenly dashed to the ground.

Voice — Abraham. Abraham. Who do you love more, your God or your son? If you love me you must take Isaac to the Land of Moriah, and sacrifice him as a burnt offering.

Scribe — Abraham couldn't believe it. He was so angry with God.

Abraham — This is completely stupid. First God gives me a son, then he takes him away again. *(Kneels down weeping)* What shall I do? I made a promise in front of everyone. I can't break it. What shall I do?

(Foreboding music marks the passage of time)

SCENE 5

(Abraham, Sarah, Isaac and two servants are asleep. Abraham wakes and then wakes Sarah and Isaac)

Scribe — One morning Abraham got up early and woke Sarah and Isaac. He saddled his ass and prepared food for the journey to Mount Moriah. He shouted at his two servants:

Abraham — Get up you layabouts. *(Shakes them)* It's about time we were going.

Servants — *(Wearily)* What time is it? What day is it?

Sarah — Come here Isaac and let me tidy your hair.

Isaac — Not now, Mum. Don't be embarrassing. We're going to worship God in the mountains.

Abraham — We must get going. We've a long day's journey ahead.

Sarah — *(Embracing Isaac)*. Take care of him, Abraham, and make sure he comes to no harm. Goodbye.

(They set out on their journey. Sarah waves)

Scribe — Sarah watched her son setting off with his father and her heart filled with pride. What a man he was going to be! She said a prayer to God that they would all be safe. *(Exit Sarah. The travellers arrive stage right)* When they reached Moriah, Abraham told the servants to stay behind while he and Isaac went up the mountain to make a sacrifice to God.

(Abraham and Isaac, carrying sticks for the fire, mime climbing the hill. The other children may sing 'Shalom, my friend' or another suitable song. When they reach the top Abraham and Isaac set the fire)

Isaac — It seems stupid making a fire when we have no lamb for the burnt offering.

Abraham — Don't worry, son. God will provide the lamb for the burnt offering.

Isaac — *(Seeing Abraham's knife)* But that knife! It frightens me! I want my mum.

Abraham — This breaks my heart, but God says that you must be the sacrifice.

Isaac — *(Agitated)* What? Are you serious? Why? Why me? God must be wrong.

Abraham — *(Weeping)* I would rather die myself. But I have made a solemn promise to God.

Isaac — I love you, dad. I don't want you to die. If it's between you and me, then let it be me. But just one thing, don't tell mum what has happened. Say . . . I have gone to live in another country.

Scribe — Then Isaac lay down on the altar. His heart was beating fast and he felt very frightened. *(Slowly and dramatically Abraham raises the knife above his head to kill Isaac)* Abraham lifted the knife above his head . . .

All — *(Shouting)* Stop, Abraham, stop! *(Abraham looks round in surprise, wondering where the shout has come from)*

Voice — Stop! Now I know that you love God more than anything else. You were even ready to give up this special child.

Isaac — Dad, what's happening?

Abraham — *(Comforting Isaac)* Don't worry. Everything's going to be all right. Listen.

Voice — 'By myself I have sworn, says the Lord: Because you have done this, and have not withheld your son, your only son, I will indeed bless you, and I will make your offspring as numerous as the stars of heaven and as the sand that is on the seashore.' Isaac and Abraham, your faith has saved your lives.

All — *(Rush to congratulate Isaac and Abraham)*

(Either triumphant music is played or a hymn sung – e.g. 'Thine be the Glory' – while the children exit)

SCENE 6

Scribe

Our story ends some years later. Isaac is grown up. Sarah has died, but Abraham is still alive and longs to see Isaac happily married. So he sends his most trusted servant to Mesopotamia, to the city of Nahor, to find Isaac a wife. Outside the city, while the servant is trying to find water for his camels, he meets a very beautiful girl called Rebekah. Immediately he knows that she is the one for Isaac. Luckily, her family agrees and she returns with the servant to marry Isaac.

At the wedding Abraham feels that he and Isaac are finally the best of friends and that any troubles from the past are now dead and buried.

(The Wedding March is played and the cast form up into a wedding procession led by Abraham, followed by bride and groom and everyone else)

All

My Son was dead and is alive (see overleaf)

Abraham and Isaac

Words and Music: Brian Mountford

Isaac and Becky join their hands today
Isaac and Becky join their hands today
Isaac and Becky join their hands today
Welcome to the Marriage Feast

Praise God from whom all blessings flow
Praise God from whom all blessings flow
Praise God from whom all blessings flow
Welcome to the marriage feast.

All *(Exit to wedding music, e.g. Wedding March, Widor's 'Toccata', Trumpet Tune ...)*

3

THE SIN BIN

This is meant for Lent and it's more a dramatic activity than a play. The theme is sin and forgiveness.

Props required are:
1. Large plastic dustbin with the words 'SIN BIN' attached.
2. Sheets of A3 paper attached to a flip chart or board.
3. A thick-nibbed felt-tipped pen.
4. A bonfire or incinerator outside.

PRESENTATION

1. Introduce the idea of the sin bin. Some children will be familiar with the term in relation to rugby league, ice hockey and American football, when players who have committed a serious foul are penalised by being made to sit out for a period in the 'sin bin'.

2. Ask children what they think we mean by 'sin' when we use the word in church, e.g. something wrong, bad, selfish, unkind, greedy, hurtful, etc.– thoughts as well as actions. Acting against God's will. Is *not* doing something ever wrong?

3. Our sin bin is of course a *dustbin*, where we put the rubbish and things we don't want. Sin is like garbage to be thrown away and destroyed. This is why we confess (own up to) sin to God and ask God's forgiveness.

4. Particular sins can be named by children. Each suggestion can be written down – preferably in one word – and the child comes forward, takes the sheet of paper, and ritually places it in the sin bin.

5. When this exercise is over, a prayer of confession may be said.

6. The bin is carried outside into the churchyard or playground, the 'sins' are emptied from the bin into the incinerator or bonfire, and someone is invited to light the fire.

7. A prayer of absolution may be said.

4

SOME MOTHERS DO 'AVE 'EM

The purpose of this section is to give a framework for presenting a Mother's Day Revue. Some or all of the material provided here may be used, and additional material may be added. The linking theme is that whatever is done emerges from the Mother's Day card.

If possible make a very large 'card' as a piece of stage scenery out of two sheets of 'eight by four' shuttering or very stiff board, hinged together at the back with wire or very strong tape. The 'card' will be seen from the inside as if opened by the reader. The 'card' can be painted with white emulsion with the words of the Mother's Day message (in the first stanza below) written with marker pen on the left-hand side, and a door cut into the right-hand side. Children will enter through this door.

INTRODUCTION

Cast: Child, Parent, Four Actors

Child *(In sentimental way)*
Dearest Mum, I know that you'll
Always be the one who's cool.
So this card is just to say
Lots of love on Mother's Day

Parent We've all written them – Mother's Day cards with appalling rhymes. Some of us (those who are mums) have received them, and however slushy they are, they're lovely! Of course, it's the thought that counts, and the home-made ones are the best.

Today, we have a very different card. Not only is it far too big to be posted in a letterbox, but it's a magic card.

(Enter Actor 1 with a magic wand through the door in the card)

Actor 1 Narnia was in the wardrobe found,
Wonderland was underground.
Rat and Mole
Lived down a hole,
But 'Mother's Day' is in this card. *(Exit)*

(Enter Actor 2 struggling with a tablet of stone)

Actor 2 It started back in years gone by
When Moses was on Sinai. *(Pronounced Sye-ni-aye)*

One day when he had time to kill
He took his note pad up the hill.

(Enter Actor 3)
Actor 3 — He had to walk (he couldn't run)
Because stone notepads weigh a ton.
The paper ones they have in schools
Are best for jotting down the rules.

(Enter Actors 4 and 1)
Actor 4 — But this job had rare requirements:
Writing down the Ten Commandments.
The one in question,

Actor 1 — Number five,

Actor 4 — Says children young and old must strive

Actor 3 — Even if they do no other

Actor 4 — To love their father and their mother.

(To audience)
Actor 1 — Honour your father and mother,

Actor 2 — Your sister, your aunt and your brother.

Actor 3 — It's the basic idea

Actor 4 — To come out of Judaea:

All — You all must love one another.

All — *(Sing)* 'A new commandment I give to you'.

JESUS IN THE TEMPLE

Cast: Three Narrators, Joseph, Mary, Jesus, Tour Guide, Two Mums

Narrator 1 — When Jesus Christ was twelve years old
One day his dad said,

Joseph — Son, behold,
Your mum and I are going down
To spend the Passover in town,
And now you're twelve, you too can come
And visit old Jerusalum.

Jesus Yippee,

Narrator 1 He said, and jumped for joy.
He was a normal little boy.

Mary There's just one thing I'd like to say,

Narrator 1 Said mother in her gentle way,

Mary It's only one of my suggestions:
But please don't ask too many questions.
I know it is the way to learn,
But you're a kid, so wait your turn.

Joseph It won't improve your father's health
To draw attention to yourself.

Narrator 2 Jerusalem that day was hectic,
The atmosphere was quite electric,
With people swarming everywhere,
The whiff of spices in the air.

Narrator 1 The Passover, a famous feast,
Attracted Jews throughout the East.
And all the kids had such a bop
That no one wanted it to stop.

Narrator 3 But all great holidays must end
Or else they'd drive you round the bend.

Narrator 2 The roads were crowded going home,
A nightmare if your child should roam.
A kid could wander round and round
With little hope of being found.

Narrator 3 That evening Mary had a hunch
She hadn't seen the boy since lunch.

Mary Joseph,

Narrator 3 She said,

Mary What shall we do?

Narrator 3 Said Jo,

Joseph I thought he'd be with you.

Narrator 1 — Then Mary panicked, in a flurry.
The tour guide said,

Tour Guide — No need to worry!
The youth club kids are always last,
They don't believe in moving fast.

Narrator 1 — Said Mary,

Mary — I shall have no peace
Until you go and call the police.

Narrator 1 — And Joseph added,

Joseph — Yes, be quick.
(Aside)
These travel agents make me sick.

Narrator 2 — The search went on till half past ten –
They searched the camp, then checked again.
His mother wept, his mother cried,

Mary — He might have let us know,

Narrator 2 — She sighed

Joseph — *(Crossly)*
I shan't give him another warning,
We'll go and find him in the morning.

Narrator 2 — So off they went at 6 a.m.
And hurried to Jerusalem.
The city streets were such a maze,
That searching for him took three days.

Narrator 3 — They found him in the Temple court,
Where the religious teachers taught.
He was discussing God with them –
This little boy with grown-up men.

Narrator 1 — And greatly to his mum's delight
He always got the answers right.
She didn't tell him that, of course,
Since she was feeling mighty cross.

Mary — What's this

Narrator 2 — She shouted looking glum,

Mary	How could you do this to your mum?
Joseph	Your mum and I've been worried stiff We thought you'd fallen down a cliff. Or been beaten up by creatures Ten times uglier than these teachers.
Mary	And now I think if you are wise, You really should apologise.
Jesus	Come off it mum. Come off it dad. I didn't mean to make you mad. If only you could understand You'd know what happened wasn't planned. Quite simply in this House of God I feel at home. D'you think that's odd?
Narrator 3	The people gathered in the court Began to mutter what they thought. One mum said,
Mum 1	It's quite atrocious Such a child should be precocious. What does he think he's playing at Discussing things of God like that?
Narrator 2	Another mum was not so fazed, She said,
Mum 2	I simply am amazed. I can see that he's prodigious, Even though I'm not religious.
Narrator 2	Then Mary said,
Mary	It's time we went.
Narrator 2	And Jesus, all obedient, Goes,
Jesus	Mum, I know you're right to scold. In future I'll do what I'm told.
Narrator 3	Before he takes another breath, They're on the way to Nazareth. When Mary thought about that day She didn't know quite what to say.

Doing a bunk was not allowed,
But then he'd made her feel so proud.

Mary — One day,

Narrator 1 — She thought when all alone,

Mary — He surely will become well known!

THE THANK YOU SKETCH

Cast: Two Presenters (either children or adults)

Props: Notepad, pencil, flip chart, 'clapometer' – i.e. board with arrow pinned onto a dial that indicates 'soft' and 'loud' on a scale of 1-10

Presenter 1 — *(With notepad and pencil)* Hello.

Presenter 2 — Hello, you look busy.

Presenter 1 — I'm making a 'thank you' list for Mother's Day

Presenter 2 — Oh really? How do you do that?

Presenter 1 — Dead easy. You get a piece of paper and you go round asking people what they want to thank their mothers for. Then you write them down and make a list.

Presenter 2 — Shall we try it, then? *(Pointing to audience)* Shall we ask these people here if there's anything they'd like to say thank you to mum for?

Presenter 1 — I've an idea. I've already got a list. So if anyone says something that's on my list, I'll cross it off, and you'll give them a sweet.

Presenter 2 — OK. Let's try it.

Presenters — *(They ask various children and adults)* What would you most like to thank your mother for?

(Answers to be written on flip chart. Presenter 1 ticks his list secretly)

THE LIST
Giving birth to me
Being there for me
Protecting me
Praising me when I've done well
Ticking me off

Helping with school work
Listening to a problem
Washing up dishes
Washing dirty socks
Cooking my tea
Housework
Earning money

Presenter 2 *(When flip chart contains seven or eight ideas)*
Now I am going to take each of these 'thank you's' in turn and ask the mothers to clap and cheer for each one. The more they like it the louder they cheer.

Presenter 1 Can we have a volunteer from the audience to work the 'clapometer'.
(Volunteer comes forward)
I want you to point this arrow to the number that you think shows how loud they are cheering.

Presenter 2 OK. Let's do it.
(The competition begins)
(When these ideas have been assessed, they are compared with the list held by Presenter 1)
(To Presenter 1) Were there any important ones on your list that they didn't get? Let's see what the mothers think of those.
(The clapometer method is used again)

Presenter 1 So the winner is . . . *(Announces the most popular 'thank you')*

Either the list above or the list on the flip chart can be used as the basis of a prayer.

PROCESSION OF FLOWERS

It is customary to give flowers to mothers on Mothering Sunday. Children can enter through the door in the stage 'card' to take flowers to their mothers.

The early part of this presentation emphasises that theologically the commandment to honour your father and your mother is part of God's overall commandment to love one another. Also in the congregation there will be mothers and grandmothers whose children are not present, and people who have not had children. It might therefore be appropriate to give flowers to all the women in church.

FOUR POEMS

THE MOST FAMOUS MUM IN THE BIBLE

The most famous mum in the Bible,
A woman without any rival,
Is probably Mary,
Though opinions may vary,
And Eve might just sue me for libel.

MUMDOM

The delights and joys of mumdom
Can sometimes be rather humdrum.
Whether to freak
When your kid gives you cheek
Is a regular conundrum.

SINGLE

Most mothers on Mother's Day tingle,
And get breakfast in bed as of course.
It's not a great day if you're single
Or if you've just had a divorce.

A family's great if you've got one –
Relationship's what it's about –
Remember that Christ never had one
And didn't do badly without.

NAMES

There's many names we use for ma,
There's mother, mum and mater,
There's mummy, mumsie and mama,
I've even heard 'tomato'.

There's many names mums use for us
There's sweetheart, love, and poppet,
There's hey, oi you, you little cuss,
Just stop that or you'll cop it.

5

EASTER CHOCOLATE

Cast: Narrator, Aziz (a shopkeeper), Josh (also Jesus), Pete, John, Jim, Jude, Teacher, Three Soldiers, Mary Magdalene, Mary the Mother of James, Joanna, Lookout, Two Bystanders , Friend.

SCENE 1

Aziz's Newsagents. (This can be created with a table and empty sweet boxes from the local newsagents.)
Children crowd round the counter picking up sweets and putting them down. It's a typical scene in any newsagents near a school.

Pop music suggestive of something sinister is playing.
Fade to . . .

Aziz (*Behind counter*) Are you going to buy those sweets?

Pete Just looking.

Aziz Because if you don't buy, you don't touch.

John There's no law against looking is there?

(*Children crowd the counter*)

Aziz Stand back, please. One at a time, please.

Jim Keep yer hair on, Aziz.

Aziz You there, don't be cheeky or you won't get served.

Jude (*Beckoning Peter, John and Jim to front of stage*) Here, you lot. Come here!
(*Stage whisper to Pete*) You see that box of chocolate eggs?

Pete Yes.

Jude I reckon if you keep Aziz busy, like talking to him or actually buying something, I could nick that box and we could flog the eggs at school and make some cash.

John What if we get caught?

Jude (*Makes sign of throat being cut*) But we won't.

Jim — And if we do, no one grasses up the others, OK? (*They shake hands on it*)

Pete — (*Strutting to counter*) Mr Aziz, you must be a saint to run this shop. (*All the children turn to listen, and laugh at the boy's cheek*) How d'you put up with all these kids giving you lip and trying to nick your sweets?

Aziz — You can say that again, you little scoundrel.

Pete — Give us a packet of the rhubarb-flavoured bubble gum, will you. (*Aziz looks for it*) It's on the shelf behind you. (*Aziz turns and climbs up to look*) No there. Right a bit, left a bit. No, sorry, right a bit. (*While his back is turned, Jude takes a large box of chocolate eggs, puts it under his coat, and ambles out of the shop with John and Jim*)

Aziz — I can't see it.

Pete — No, they don't make rhubarb flavour. (*Wags finger at Aziz*) Just checking!

All — (*Laugh*)

Aziz — Go on, get out. Get out all of you. I've had enough of you.

(*Music – preferably suggestive of school.*
Actors each take a chair from back of stage and re-group as a class of children in school)

SCENE 2

Narrator — The next day in school, before the teacher arrives in the classroom, the four shoplifters try to sell the stolen Easter eggs.

(*Jude, Pete, John and Jim use Josh's desk as a shop counter. The box of sweets is on it. One child is posted to look out for the teacher*)

Jude — Roll up. Roll up. Lovely cut-price sweets. Chocolate eggs only 20p. Quickly before Miss Budd comes.

(*Various children make a purchase. This part of the scene should be improvised*)

Look out! She's here. Quick, she's here.

(*But they are not quick enough, and the box of eggs is left on Josh's desk while all scamper to their seats.*

Enter teacher who immediately sees the sweets)

Teacher — Whose is this box of chocolate eggs?

(*Silence*)

Teacher — Are they yours, Josh?

Josh — No Miss.

Teacher — Whose are they then?

(*Silence*)

Teacher — Who brought them into school? Did you Tom? Did you Jude?

(*Silence*)

Teacher — This is a very serious matter. The Head has received a phone call from Mr Aziz at the Newsagent's to say that a box of chocolate Easter eggs has been stolen from his shop. Now who is going to own up?

(*Silence*)

Teacher — Who brought the eggs into school?

Jude — (*Pointing at Josh*) He did, Miss.

(*A gasp of disbelief goes round the room*)

Teacher — Did you, Josh?

Josh — No Miss.

Teacher — Can you tell me who did, then?

Josh — No Miss.

Teacher — Then I shall have to keep you all in after school until we find out the truth. I can't believe that Josh did this, but with the evidence on his desk I think he had better go to the Head's office at once.

All — That's not fair, Miss.

(*Music to create mood for Passiontide drama.*
Exit Teacher. Children remove chairs to back of stage)

SCENE 3

(*Garden of Gethsemane.*
Jesus is kneeling centre stage. Around him, sleeping, are the disciples)

Narrator — Class 8 has been preparing some Easter scenes for school assembly. By chance, Josh plays the part of Jesus and the children involved in the shoplifting scandal are disciples. We are going to watch their dress rehearsal. The first scene is in the garden of Gethsemane. It is the night that Jesus was arrested and darkness is falling amongst the olive trees.

(*Pause*)

Josh/Jes — (*Praying*) Our Father, who art in heaven, hallowed be thy name. Thy Kingdom come. Thy will be done on earth as it is in heaven. Give us this day our daily bread, and forgive us our trespasses as we forgive those who trespass against us.

(*Enter Jude and three soldiers (or more) shouting*)

And lead us not into temptation, but deliver us from evil . . .

Soldier 1 — Where is he, Judas?

Jude — Over there.

Soldier 1 — Where? I can't see him.

Soldier 2 — Give me a light.

Soldier 3 — (*Falling and making a great fuss*) Ouch! I've twisted my ankle.

Soldier 1 — Come on Judas.

Jude — The one I kiss is your man. This is your best chance to arrest him.

Soldier 2 — Go on then. Hurry up.

Soldier 3 — Earn your money, Judas. Thirty pieces of silver's not bad for a night's work.

(*The disciples wake and begin to group behind Jesus. Judas approaches Jesus and greets him with a formal embrace*)

Jude — Greetings Rabbi!

(*The soldiers grab Jesus and hold him tight as he faces the audience*)

Jesus — Do you think I'm a robber? You don't need your swords and clubs. I've been teaching in the Temple every day this week. Why didn't you arrest me there?

Soldier 1 — (*Twisting his arm*) Don't listen to his cheek.

Soldier 2 — Come on, to the high priest's house.

Soldier 3 — Let's see what he has to say for himself there. (*Laughs*)

Soldier 1 — (*Mocking*) We'll soon see who really is King of the Jews.

John — Leave him alone. He's done nothing wrong.

Soldier 1 — (*Threatening*) You shut your face, or I'll shut it for you.

Jim — He's innocent. I know. He's done nothing wrong.

Soldier 2 — Shut up, you creep.

Soldier 3 — Take no notice. If you ask me, they're all religious nutters. (*Throws bag of money to Judas who takes it and runs away*)
Let's go.

Disciples — (*Shouting*) No. No. Let go. Leave him.

(*They try to intervene but are thrown off.*
Jesus is led away and turns to look plaintively at the disciples, who run away)

(*Atmospheric music*)

SCENE 4

Narrator — The next night the disciples who had deserted Jesus met at a friend's house. (*The disciples – except Judas – looking glum, enter and take a chair to front of stage. Some sit, some stand*) They wondered what they would do without Jesus. Would they ever see him again? They were shocked and confused. They didn't really understand what had happened.

Pete — I wish we hadn't run away.

John — Did you see his face as he looked back at us?

Jim — He looked frightened.

Pete — So would you.

Pete I'm sorry we left him alone.

John I wish we could turn the clock back.

Jim Perhaps we'll get it right next time.

(They begin to sing 'Jesus Forgive Me' which is repeated like a chant, and as they sing the whole cast comes forward to join in)

Jesus Forgive Me

Words and Music: Brian Mountford

All *(Non-disciples return to places away from central stage)*

Narrator Later, the women who had followed Jesus to his crucifixion came to the house where the disciples were gathered. (*Joanna, Mary Magdalene and Mary the mother of James enter and are seated*) When the disciples saw Mary Magdalene, Joanna, and Mary the mother of James, they asked to be told about everything that had happened.

Mary M (*Moves to front of stage and speaks to audience*) It was awful. We stood outside the Roman fortress and Pilate came out onto the balcony and asked, 'What shall I do with Jesus, the King of the Jews?' Everyone shouted:

All Crucify him. Crucify him. (*Chanting to a frenzy*) We have no king but Caesar. We have no king but Caesar.

Joanna (*To audience*) They made him carry his own cross, but he kept falling down. Veronica ran out of the crowd with a handkerchief and wiped his face, but the soldiers threw her back.

Mary J (*To audience*) Then they forced Simon from Cyrene to carry the cross for him.

Mary M When they reached Calvary, they nailed him to the cross. (*She falters, but regains her dignity*) People were shouting and swearing, but he was quiet. Then he said, 'Father forgive them, for they know not what they do.'

Jim What happened next?

Joanna They crucified two criminals with him – robbers, scum of the earth – one on his right and the other on his left. The crowd were taunting Jesus:

Bystander 1 (*Shouts from audience*) If you are the Son of God, why don't you come down from the cross?

Bystander 2 (*From audience*) He saved others but he cannot save himself!

All (*Jeering in their own words*)

(*Play dramatic recorded music for 30 seconds. All actors stand and look up at the sky. Fade to . . .*)

Narrator At about three o'clock in the afternoon the sun darkened and people began to panic. It was probably an eclipse of the sun, but they thought the end of the world had come. Some said the veil of the Temple had been torn in two.

(*A drum beats solemnly behind the high altar, or at the back of the theatre. The actors look toward the sound of the drum*)

Jesus cried out with a loud voice. Some said:

All He is calling for Elijah.

Narrator — Then, hardly able to breathe any more, he prayed to God, 'Father, into your hands I commend my spirit.' And he died.

(*Long pause*)

Pete — That's really the end, isn't it? What shall we do now?

Mary M — What is there we can do?
(*All exit.*
Passiontide hymn)

SCENE 5

In the classroom.
Taking their chairs the children, except Josh, re-group as a school class.

Narrator — I expect you're wondering what happened about Mr Aziz's box of chocolate eggs. Well, later that day, after school, Class 8 waited nervously for their teacher, Miss Budd, to arrive. When there was trouble Miss Budd could be quite scary.

(*Enter Miss Budd*)

Teacher — The Head and I are extremely concerned about Mr Aziz's box of chocolate eggs. At this moment Josh is in the Head's office being interviewed by Constable Perkins, our local policeman. In a minute each of you in turn will be questioned by him. (*Looks searchingly at the class*)

Jude — (*Raises his hand*)

Teacher — Yes, Jude?

Jude — Please Miss, I don't think it's fair for Josh to be questioned by himself.

Teacher — Why not?

Jude — Because . . . you see . . .

Teacher — Go on.

Jude — Because . . . I can't say, Miss.

Mary M — I don't think it's fair either, Miss. He didn't do it.

Teacher — Then who did do it, Mary?

Mary I'm not sure, Miss.

Pete I don't think it's fair, either . . . he definitely didn't do it.

Teacher So you know who did do it?

Pete Yes, Miss.

Teacher I think you had better tell me, don't you, Peter?

Pete (*Nods*)

Teacher Was it you?

Pete Might have been.

Teacher Just you and nobody else? (*Silence*) If there was anyone else, would they please stand up now.

(*Jude, John and Jim slowly and reluctantly stand up. Pete also stands*)

Thank you. (*Pause*) I know that took a lot of courage.
But why this change of heart?

Pete It was the play, Miss – the play for assembly. When we were acting all that stuff about Judas . . .

(*The following six lines are repeated from Scene 4*)

John 'And what about Judas? That was the dirtiest trick I've ever seen.'

Pete 'He deserves to die for that.'

Jim 'I feel like I'd betrayed Jesus too.'

Pete 'Grassed him up . . .'

John 'Let him down . . .'

Jim 'I just feel so guilty.'

Pete 'I'm sorry we left him alone.'
It made us think about Josh, Miss.

Jude I think that's why we've owned up.

(*Music.*
All exit, taking chairs to back of stage. Pete, John and Jim move quickly, and preferably unseen, to the back of the auditorium)

SCENE 6

Narrator — The final scene Class 8 rehearsed for their assembly was about a stranger who nobody recognised.

On the Sunday after Good Friday, some of the disciples set out from Jerusalem to visit friends in Emmaus, a village about eight miles away.

(*Pete, John and Jim walk from the back of the auditorium to the stage*)

As they walked along the road they were talking about Jesus' death, and how he had once said that if he were killed he would rise again from the dead. Then they met the stranger.

(*They reach the stage where they meet Josh/Jes who is crossing the stage*)

Josh/Jes — What's up? Why are you looking so miserable? Anyone would have thought you'd seen a ghost. Have you had bad news?

Jim — You must be a stranger round here.

John — Haven't you heard?

Josh/Jes — Heard what?

Jim — About Jesus of Nazareth, of course. He was crucified the day before yesterday. Everyone's talking about it.

John — We thought he was going to save the world.

Pete — But we ran away and left him, and now he is dead.

Josh/Jes — Are you sure? Didn't the prophets say that the Messiah must suffer before he enters into his glory?

John — This morning our friends thought they saw angels who told them he is alive again.

Jim — But they probably imagined it.

(*They mime the journey as best fits the church or acting space*)

Narrator — As they walked on they saw the roofs of Emmaus climbing like a staircase up the hillside. The sun was beginning to set and at the end of an exhausting day they were beginning to feel hungry. The stranger said he had further to travel, but the disciples persuaded him to stay for supper.

(*All the children form a tableau around a table set with a loaf of bread and a carafe of wine with goblets. During the next short narration the travellers arrive at the house – stage left*)

Children were playing and shouting, and a donkey was kicking its hooves against the cobbles, as they climbed the slope of the alley that led to their friend's house.
(*They knock at the door*)

Friend (*Greeting each one*) Welcome. Come in. It's great to see you.

Pete (*Introducing Jesus*) We met this man on the road and asked him to supper.

Friend (*Taking Jesus to the head of the table*) Of course. Make yourself at home. I am honoured to have you as a guest in my house. You must sit at the head of the table. Will you give thanks before we eat?

(*The friend and disciples sit down in their places. There is a dramatic pause*)

Jesus (*Stands. Lifts up the loaf*)
Blessed are you, Lord God of all creation. Through your goodness we have this bread to offer, which earth has given and human hands have made. It will become for us the bread of life.

All Blessed be God for ever.

(*Jesus breaks the loaf*)

Pete (*Whispers*) It's Jesus.

John (*Louder*) It is Jesus.

All (*Not in unison*) Yes, it's Jesus. (*Silence as Jesus distributes the bread to the actors*)

Jesus (*Lifts up the wine*)
Blessed are you, Lord God of all creation. Through your goodness we have this wine to offer. Fruit of the vine and work of human hands, it will become our spiritual drink.

All Blessed be God for ever.

The Road to Emmaus

Words and Music: Brian Mountford

'O how foolish you are
And so slow in believing',
Said the stranger to us
As we walked down the road.
'Remember the prophets,
What they said in their preaching,
That Jesus must suffer
Then rise from the dead.'

At the end of the day
When the stars were appearing,
He had nowhere to go
So we pressed him to stay.
As he shared out the bread
And praised God with a blessing,
We knew it was Jesus,
Our life and our way.

(Chorus)

6

FUNKY PARABLES

THE SOWER OF THE YEAR

A parable based on Luke 8:5–15

This can be spoken by children aged 10–12 and acted by younger children. Lines may be divided between several children, each one saying two at a time. The lines should not be hurried, giving plenty of time for younger children to mime.

*Cast: Readers, Sower, Seeds, Birds, Thistles and 'Hearers of the word'**

I guess there's more you'd like to know
About the sower who went to sow.
The people that I've asked, who knew,
Said when he passed the seeds just flew.

They whirred, and whizzed, at lightning speed,
Like camels in a wild stampede.
He really didn't seem to care –
In fact, he chucked them everywhere.

Of average height, with suntanned skin,
Great hairy arms and bearded chin,
This local farmer from Judea
Was voted Sower of the Year.

A lot of seeds fell on the road
(In conflict with the Highway Code).
The birds above said, 'Thanks a bunch!
Let's flutter down and have some lunch!'

Some seed was thrown on stony ground
And since there was no soil around,
It sprung up fast – it pranced and bragged –
But when the sun came out it flagged.

Some seed was cast amongst the thorns
And never made it into corn:
Before the little seedlings spread,
The thistles grew and choked them dead.

The soil on which the others fell
Was fertile, which was just as well!
Or else there'd be no tale to tell,
No punch line to this 'parabelle'!

The seeds that hit the fertile earth
Grew healthy plants that proved their worth.
The best seeds made a hundred more –
Which pleased the farmer that's for sure.

So now you'd like to ask, no doubt,
What is this story all about?
The secret's quite a simple one:
God throws his love at everyone.

The question then we must pursue
Is will God's love take root in you?
Or like the seeds that hit the deck
Just finish down some birdie's neck?

The people on the rocks are rash,
And get religious in a flash.
As soon as things don't go their way,
They start to sulk and go away.

The thorn-choked types are people who'll
Be keen on God, and say 'God's cool',
Until a mate says, 'Wait a minute,
There isn't any money in it!'

Now anyone whose soil is deep
Ain't necessarily a creep.
But probably the groovy kind
Who thinks of God with open mind.

The thing I want you all to know
Is people reap what people sow.
And if it's *love* you sow, don't stop,
You're bound to get the biggest crop.

When Jesus told this funky tale
He hoped the story wouldn't fail
To make his meaning very clear:
'You who have ears to hear, then HEAR'.

THE BIRTHDAY BASH
A parable based on Luke 14: 7–11

Of all the things we can't resist
By far the worst is selfishness.
The story we're about to tell
Describes the symptoms very well.

Your best friend has a birthday bash
At some hotel that's very flash,
(You see her dad is rolling in it
And spoils her rotten once a minute).

Anyway, you've been invited,
And you're feeling so excited,
You go and buy a brand new dress,
Designer labelled to impress.

Your purpose, when all's said and done,
Is they should know you're *number one*.
Let no one think you're like the rest –
As *best friend*, you're the special guest.

Her dad is standing at the door
And says, 'Good Afternoon, I'm sure.
You must be Jill, or are you Jane?
You little girls all look the same.'

'I'm June,' you say, all smiles and grace,
But wish he'd go and boil his face.
(Just because he's got some money
Doesn't mean you find him funny.)

Besides the ritzy grand hotel
They've hired a conjuror as well.
The conjuror needs for his pretence
A helper from the audience.

And you, as if about to burst,
Shout and bellow, 'Me first, me first'.
'Shut up you brat. It's time to learn
When to pipe down and take your turn.'

'Jemima, *darling*,' yells her mum,
As if her mouth contained a plum,
'Since you're the birthday girl, it's *you*
Should be the one that's sawn in two'.

Her mother's words leave you upset.
You think, 'Oh yuk, she's *mummy's pet.*
Jemima might be my best friend
But may she have a sticky end.'

The conjuror does his best to please,
But she emerges in one piece.
And when the clock strikes half past three,
A footman booms, 'It's time for tea.

'Young persons will you take your seats
And tuck into the birthday eats?'
To you the thing that matters most
Is sitting down beside your host.

You lift your skirt and make a dash;
You grab the best seat in a flash.
The footman says, 'You little tyke!
That's acting most *unladylike*.'

You pout your lips and growl, 'So what?
Some *person's* got to have this spot.'
Her mother yells, 'Not you, my dear.
Jem's Cousin Harold must sit here.

'He's travelled from the USA
Especially to be here today –
All the way from Carolina
To *visit with* our dear Jemima.

'Perhaps you'd take your plate and spoon
And sit down in the other room.'
You tell yourself, 'This can't be true!'
But every eye seems fixed on you.

You feel the biggest freak in town
As you get up and he sits down.
A voice shouts out, 'She's gone bright red.
I bet she wishes she was dead.'

And so you leave Jemima there,
With Cousin Harold in your chair,
And end this very special day
Wishing you could fade away.

The moral of this little tale
Is pushiness is bound to fail.
Unselfishness is in the end
The only way to make a friend.

THE CHURCH-GOER AND THE JUNKIE

A parable based on Luke 18: 9–14

The sort of kid I like the most
Will never brag and doesn't boast.
The sort of kid I most detest
Will always tell you, 'I'm the best.'

This arrogance is nothing new,
It happens in most adults too.
But worst of all (I'll tell you now)
Are those who're *holier-than-thou.*

This story is about a guy
Who rates his chances very high
Of getting on with God so well
The rest of us can go to hell.

Now just suppose for one weekend
You visit London with a friend,
And, feeling rich, you hire a cabby
To take you to Westminster Abbey.

And there outside the great West door
(A sight you've never seen before)
Two men are praying, both aloud,
One is humble, the other proud.

'I am, praise God,' the proud one smirks,
'A pillar of the local church.
Thank God I'm not a rogue or cheat,
Or doing drugs out on the street.

'I count myself extremely blest
To be more holy than the rest.
And though I know I'm not *quite* perfect,
I'm better than this sad drug addict.'

The junkie simply bowed his head
And started weeping as he said,
'Be merciful almighty God,
I've been a really stupid clod.

'I'm in a mess, please hear my prayer,
I need some tender loving care.
My life is like it's down the drain.
I'd like to die and start again.'

'Which of these two?' you ask your friend,
'Will find true happiness in the end?'
'We know!' we say with one accord,
'Whichever one is not a fraud.'

The lesson to be learnt, methinks,
Is *showing off to God* just stinks,
While being humble, true, and meek
Is pleasant, honest, cool, and *chic*.

THE BIG PIZZA SUPPER
A parable based on Luke 14: 16–24

One day my dad says, 'Look here, son,
I think it's time we had some fun.
I like a "beano" now and then:
You want a treat? Just tell me when.

Invite your mates. We'll make a list
And lay on food they can't resist.
I won't accept an "if" or "but",
I'll phone and book the *Pizza Hut*.

'Quick, fetch your mum, we'll fix a date.
Great stuffed crust pizzas! I can't wait!
Mozarella, Pepperoni,
Margherita, Canelloni,

'Extra prawn Napolitana,
Garlic with Siciliana,
I love them – so crisp, and crunchy,
Light and fluffy, fresh and munchy –

'Chicken feast with extra topping!
Son, I see your eyes are popping.
Lemonade and coke and soda –
Oh the joy, the heavenly odour!

'I'll get the waitresses to wear
A crown of daisies in their hair.
I hope that every single guest
Will say, "That party was the best." '

'Hey, Pops, calm down, I think you may
Just be getting carried away.
'You've started foaming through your beard –
No wonder that they say you're weird!'

The invitations soon were sent
To boys and girls from Leeds to Kent.
And very soon replies were penned
From children who could not attend.

The message in the first dispatch
Was, 'Sorry, got a football match.
I'd like to come, but Saturday
The match is being played away.'

Then number two, whose name was Bruce,
Soon telephoned with his excuse:
'I've bought that bike I talked about,
And have to go and try it out.'

The third one said, 'Dear Dave, how nice!
Your party sounds like paradise,
But now I'm going out with Jim
I want to spend more time with him.'

A fourth (a kid not in St Luke)
Had been invited by a fluke.
'I've been instructed by my mum
To get my hair cut, so *can't come*.'

Hearing this, my Dad yells, 'Stop!'
He went bright red and blew his top.
'All I hear are these excuses!
Beware whoever next refuses!

'If those spoiled brats don't want my spread,
Then search the streets and lanes instead.
Bring in the swats, the teacher's pets;
Invite the creeps, the sneaks, the wets.

'And ask the homeless and the poor –
There's loads of room for plenty more.
They won't do this "*excuse me*" stuff;
They'll think my pizza's good enough.'

So what's the meaning of this rhyme?
Well, Heaven is Pizza Party time,
And if you're asked, don't mess about,
Say yes at once, or you'll miss out.

THE DENTIST WITH THE WICKED GRIN

A parable based on Luke 10: 25–37

A lawyer, by the name of Weber,
Said bluntly, 'Please define a *neighbour*.'
If Jesus were around today,
He might have answered in this way:

*

The thing most children cannot bear
Is sitting in the dentist's chair.
What kind of *demon* likes the job
Of drilling holes inside your gob?

'Sit back,' he says, 'This doesn't hurt.
You'll only feel a little squirt.'
Then, 'Help, oh yoiks!' the needle's in,
And thus the torture doth begin.

'Mouth open wide.' Four eyes peer in:
The dentist with his wicked grin,
And on his left, in nurse's kit,
The lady who sucks out the spit.

The child who features in this scene
Had left the dentist's pretty green,
Having had an hour of drilling
Followed by a rotten filling.

And now no longer beautiful,
His cheeks seem stuffed with cotton wool.
'I can't be seen like this,' he said,
'I'll walk home through the park instead.'

But halfway home he heard a noise –
Out jumped a gang of older boys.
The leader showed an ugly fist,
And through his vicious lips he hissed,

'This park can be dangerous place,
And I'm not sure I like your face.
In fact you look a proper loon
All puffed up like an air balloon.

'Let's get him, boys, the little rat,
We'll teach him not to look like that.'

And so they beat him for a lark,
And left him lying in the park.

His ribs are bruised, his mouth is cut,
He has a very painful nut!
And since they've also smashed his case,
There's homework flying round the place.

By chance a priest walks by that way.
'Please help!' our victim tries to say.
'I've got a meeting, sorry mate,
I mustn't stop or I'll be late.'

A social worker next comes past.
'Oh great,' he thinks, 'here's help at last.'
The lady says, 'You little Turk,
I get enough of this at work.'

How does he feel? Of course, you've guessed –
This treatment makes him feel depressed.
But when he thinks the end is nigh
Hears friendly footsteps passing by.

The boy forlornly lifts his chin –
Lo and behold, that *wicked grin.*
'I know my treatment's hit and miss,
But surely not as bad as *this*!

'What's happened to you my poor child?
Let's help you up,' the dentist smiled.
And with some ointment from his case,
The dentist soothed the poor boy's face.

'I'm going to take you home – it's late –
We'll get a taxi at the gate.
To tease your mum, I'll say, "Beware
Of ever having dental care!" '

*

Now which of these three, would you say,
Was neighbour to the boy that day?
The lawyer said, 'The kindest one.'
Well, go and do the same, my son.

THE PRODIGAL RAP
(A parable based on Luke 15: 11–32)

In a very big house in Palestine
Lived a man who had made a fortune from wine.
He had servants and slaves, so the story runs.
He was married to his wife and they had two sons.

Simon (the older) was a bit of a clot,
He never went out, and moaned a lot.
But Jacob (the younger) was quite a lad,
He stayed out late, which worried his dad.

One day in the holidays at half past one
He rolled out of bed and said to his mum,
'Please give me some money 'cos I'm going to town.'
'Your father won't like it, so just slow down.'

When his dad got home, said Jake, 'I'm bored.
Just give me some money, 'cos I'm going abroad.'
Said dad to his son, 'I'm not very keen,
You're on probation and you're only fourteen.'

'You don't understand. I'm a very cool dude.'
Said mum, 'What we hate is your at-ti-tude.
At your age, my dear, we were never this bad.'
'Oh, leave it out, mum, and don't be sad.'

Now doting parents can often be soft,
So Jake got some plastic, and then he was off.
Down to the bank as quick as a flash –
At the hole in the wall, filled his pockets with cash.

His first port of call was the 'Twenty One Club'
Where an older mate said, 'Let's go to the pub.'
Outside the pub sat his girlfriend, Delilah,
Who lived out rough with her pet Rottweiler.

Said Jake to his friends, 'The drinks are on me.
I've got some money, so now we are free.'
Said Delilah to Jake, 'You're a really ace bloke,
So get us some fags and we'll all have a smoke.'

'We'll hire a car, and Delilah can drive,
And we'll go to a place where we'll all feel alive.'
It was great, it was cool, and they stayed up late,
In a far off town, in a far off state.

(Slower)
One day at the bank, the clerk said, 'Sonny,
I'm very, very sorry, but you've run out of money.'
Said Jake to the clerk, 'This must be a joke.'
Said the bank clerk to Jake, 'My son, you are broke.'

Delilah was hard, and said, 'Jake you're a fool.
I'm leaving you now for your mate, 'cos he's cool.'
Jake sat all alone on the pavement and cried,
But he couldn't go home – he'd rather have died!

He said to himself, 'I must not be a snob.
I'll go off at once and find me a job.'
Swilling out pigs was the best he could get
At two pounds an hour and a great deal of sweat.

At the end of the day he was totally shattered,
But paying off his debts was all that mattered.
'I'm hungry,' said Jake, 'And I feel quite ill –
So hungry, in fact, I could eat this swill.'

That night he was restless and tried to pray,
Then suddenly saw where the answer lay:
'I'm such an idiot, I must be mad,
I'll swallow my pride and go home to dad.

'He has servants at home on twice my pay.
I'll ask for forgiveness and then I shall say,
"I know I've done wrong and things have slid,
I'm no longer worthy to be called your kid." '

So he set off home expecting the worst –
He needn't have worried 'cos his dad spoke first:
'Well, it's great to see you, you silly young thug.
Come a bit closer and give me a hug.'

'Dad, I know I've done wrong and things have slid,
And I'm no longer worthy to be called your kid.'
'It's great that you're home, and you're safe at least,
We'll invite all our friends and we'll have a feast.

'Go down to the shops and buy some new gear.
We'll soon have a party atmosphere.
I'll hire a marquee and order a band –
I'm the happiest father in all the land.'

When his older brother heard the music play
He said to the servants, 'So what's on today?'

'Oh, haven't you heard, your brother is back,
And your father's acting like a maniac.'

Well, Simon was angry and blew his top,
And rudely crashed the 'Welcome Home' bop.
'Dad, for years I've worked here for you like a slave,
And when did you ever see me misbehave?

'I've been an example of a loyal son;
He's wasted your money on drinking and fun;
You've never given *me* the smallest treat –
When *he* comes home you invite the whole street!'

'Son, don't be so jealous; what is mine is yours,
So come on inside and close all the doors.
It's time to rejoice and to cut out strife,
Your brother was dead and has come back to life.'

7

HARVEST

Jesus used stories from the farming year to illustrate his teaching about the Kingdom of God. Seedtime represents the preaching of the Good News, and harvest the gathering of people into the Kingdom. John the Baptist said (Matthew 3:12) that after the harvest Christ would separate the wheat from the chaff, and store the grain and burn the chaff.

In Jesus' teaching, harvest is inseparable from the preaching of the Good News and our response to it.

The story of Brother John's Sermon, which follows, is about spreading the Good News of the gospel. This can be used in conjunction with 'The Sower of the Year', 'The Big Pizza Supper', or 'The Prodigal Rap' in 'Funky Parables'.

At Harvest Festival the theme of seedtime and harvest makes two obvious spiritual points:

1. How we respond to the life and teaching of Jesus.
2. Jesus affirms the place of celebration in Christian life. The emphasis should therefore be on thanksgiving for the gifts of the earth.

BROTHER JOHN'S SERMON

VERSION 1 DRAMATIC FORM

Cast: *Narrator, Abbot, John, Bishop, Child.*

(*Narrator at lectern. Abbot seated centre stage*)

Narrator: Brother John was a new boy at the monastery and was finding it hard to settle down to his new way of life. (*John approaches the Abbot*) One day the Abbot called Brother John into his study and said,

Abbot: Brother John, I want you to preach the sermon next Sunday.

John: What me? But I'm only a new boy! I'm not used to giving sermons.

Abbot: Well perhaps you'll have something *new* to say.

Narrator: The next Sunday there was a large congregation in the abbey church. (*John climbs pulpit*) When the time for the sermon came, Brother John could hardly climb the pulpit steps because his knees were knocking so badly. The echo in the great building seemed to roar as if he were about to be eaten alive.

John (*Nervously*) My brothers and sisters, do you know what I am going to say?

All No!

John Well, neither do I! (*Leaves pulpit and approaches Abbot*)

Narrator Next morning the Abbot summoned him to his study.

John (*To audience*) Oh dear, this could be tricky.

Abbot Well, Brother John that wasn't very good was it? I want you to have another go next week. And may the Lord be with you.

John (*To audience*) He'll need to be.

Narrator The following Sunday the same thing happened. The abbey was even more crowded than usual because people had come specially to hear the peculiar new preacher. But they had agreed amongst themselves that if he tried the same trick as last time they would catch him out. (*John climbs pulpit*) Up the steps he climbed trembling with fright and looked out into the great gaping mouth of the church.

John My brothers and sisters, do you know what I'm going to say?

All Yes.

John (*Thinks for a moment*) Well, I've no need to tell you then, have I? (*Leaves pulpit and approaches Abbot*)

Narrator Next morning the Abbot summoned him to his study.

John (*To audience*) Oh dear, this could be ticklish.

Abbot Well, Brother John that wasn't any better was it? I'm going to give you one more chance. I want you to preach again next week and you might be interested to know that the Bishop will be with us. So it had better be good. And may the Lord be with you.

John (*To audience*) He wasn't much use last time.

(*Enter Bishop wearing cope – possibly to fanfare*)

Narrator The word had spread about Brother John's sermons and the following Sunday there were so many people they were standing in the aisles. When the Bishop arrived he said to the Abbot,

Bishop	It's nice to see so many people. You obviously told them I was coming.
Abbot	Well, actually . . . (*Thinks for a moment*) Well, it's amazing how the word spreads.
Narrator	Said the Abbot, not wanting to tell a lie. Meanwhile the congregation had laid a plan to trap Brother John which they were certain couldn't fail. (*John climbs pulpit*) So Brother John climbed the pulpit steps and looked out at the grinning faces of the vast congregation.
John	My brothers and sisters, do you know what I'm going to say?
All	(*One group of children shouts*) Yes. (*Another group of children shouts*) No.
Child	Get out of that one if you can.
John	(*Thinks for a moment*) Then those who said 'yes' can tell those who said 'no'. (*Leaves pulpit and approaches Abbot*)
Narrator	After the service the Abbot summoned John to the vestry.
John	(*To audience*) Yoiks, this time he's really going to blow his top.
Abbot	The Bishop and I want to congratulate you on your excellent sermon. I have never known our congregation to be so friendly towards each other, and you are quite right to say that we must tell other people about the Good News of Jesus.
Bishop	Well done, Brother John. I am so glad that I was able to attract such a large congregation to hear you.
John	May the Lord be with you, Bishop.
Abbot	Hey, I think that's my line!
	(*All exit*)

VERSION 2

Brother John was a new boy at the monastery and was finding it hard to settle down to his new way of life.

One day the Abbot called Brother John into his study and said, 'Brother John, I want you to preach the sermon next Sunday.'

'What me?' exclaimed Brother John. 'But I'm only a new boy! I'm not used to giving sermons.'
'Well perhaps you'll have something *new* to say,' said the Abbot.

The next Sunday there was a large congregation in the abbey church. When the time for the sermon came, Brother John could hardly climb the pulpit steps because his knees were knocking so badly. The echo in the great building seemed to roar as if he were about to be eaten alive.
'My brothers and sisters,' stammered Brother John. 'Do you know what I am going to say?'
'No,' they all shouted.
'Well, neither do I!' he said, and he backed timidly out of the pulpit and returned to his stall.

Next morning the Abbot summoned him to his study. 'Oh dear,' thought John, 'this could be tricky.'
'Well, Brother John,' sighed the Abbot, 'that wasn't very good was it? I want you to have another go next week. And may the Lord be with you.'
'He'll need to be,' said John under his breath.

The following Sunday the same thing happened. The abbey was even more crowded than usual because people had come specially to hear the peculiar new preacher. But they had agreed amongst themselves that if he tried the same trick as last time they would catch him out. Up the steps he climbed trembling with fright and looked out into the great gaping mouth of the church.

'My brothers and sisters,' he began. 'Do you know what I'm going to say?'
'Yes,' they all shouted. He paused.
'Well, I've no need to tell you then, have I?' said John, and he left the pulpit.

Next morning the Abbot summoned him to his study. 'Oh dear,' thought John, 'this could be ticklish.'
'Well, Brother John,' sighed the Abbot, 'that wasn't any better was it? I'm going to give you one more chance. I want you to preach again next week and you might be interested to know that the Bishop will be with us. So it had better be good. And may the Lord be with you.'
'He wasn't much use last time,' muttered John under his breath.

The word had spread about Brother John's sermons and the following Sunday there were so many people that they were standing in the aisles. When the Bishop arrived he said to the Abbot, 'It's nice to see so many people. You obviously told them I was coming.'
'Well, actually . . .' The Abbot thought for a moment. 'Well, it's amazing how the word spreads,' he said, not wanting to tell a lie. Meanwhile the congregation had laid a plan to trap Brother John which they were certain couldn't fail. So Brother John climbed the pulpit steps and looked out at the grinning faces of the vast congregation.

'My brothers and sisters,' he began. 'Do you know what I'm going to say?' One half of the congregation said 'Yes', and the other half said 'No.' 'Get out of that one,' shouted a voice from the back.
'Then those who said yes can tell those who said no,' said John, and he turned round and came down the pulpit steps back to his place.

After the service the Abbot summoned John to the vestry. 'Yoiks,' thought John, 'this time he's really going to blow his top.'

'The Bishop and I want to congratulate you on your excellent sermon,' said the Abbot, smiling. 'I have never known our congregation to be so friendly towards each other, and you are quite right to say that we must tell other people about the Good News of Jesus.'
'Well done, Brother John,' said the Bishop. 'I am so glad that I was able to attract such a large congregation to hear you.'
'May the Lord be with you,' said John.
'I think that's my line,' said the Abbot.

8

SUMMARY OF REQUIREMENTS FOR THE THREE PLAYS

ABRAHAM AND ISAAC

CAST
Fourteen (3 male, 3 female, 8 male or female).

AGE RANGE
8 – 13 with younger children as dancers if required.

APPROXIMATE RUNNING TIME
20 –25 minutes.

MUSIC
One song in text. Other songs and hymns are suggested in text, but producer may choose.
Recorded music for dancing and mood setting between scenes.

SET
Bare stage except for table and chair for scribe. Other scenery may be provided if desired.
Props as instructed.

SYNOPSIS
Abraham has nightmares about the day he nearly sacrificed Isaac to God. The story of Isaac's birth and childhood is then told, including the day of 'sacrifice'. The play is resolved by the enactment of Isaac's marriage to Rebekah, when Abraham and Isaac are finally reconciled in a sort of 'resurrection' scene.

MRS NOAH'S LAST STAND

CAST
Thirteen. (It is best for Shem, Ham and Japheth, to be played by boys and their wives by girls. All other parts, including Noah, can be played by boys or girls. There is some added humour in having Passing Man played by an adult.)

AGE RANGE
3–13 with younger children as animals.

APPROXIMATE RUNNING TIME
25 – 30 minutes.

MUSIC
Songs with piano accompaniment. Suggestions in text.
Sound effect CD of 'Weather' for rain and storm.

SET
The Ark. A 'rainbow' – for the last scene.

SYNOPSIS
God warns Noah of the ensuing flood that will drown the unrighteous and suggests that Noah should build an ark to save his family. The family set about this task. Mrs Noah is extremely sceptical about the whole project. They check in the animals. Mrs Noah thinks it is wrong to leave friends behind, but finally she is forced on board. The rains come for forty days and forty nights.

Noah releases a raven and a dove to look for dry land. When Noah and his family discover they have been saved, they praise God who sends a rainbow as a promise that such a fate will never befall humankind again.

EASTER CHOCOLATE

CAST
Eighteen (5 male, 3 female, 10 male or female).

AGE RANGE
8 – 12

APPROXIMATE RUNNING TIME
25 – 30 minutes.

MUSIC
'Jesus forgive me' and 'The Road to Emmaus' – words and music in text. Other hymns or songs suggested, but producer may choose.
Recorded pop and passiontide music.
Drum.

SET
A sweet shop counter. A chair for each actor for 'classroom' scenes. At least one desk (for Josh) from which sweets are sold in class.
Table, bread and wine for 'Emmaus' scene.

SYNOPSIS
Sweets are stolen from Aziz's Sweet Shop, but the children responsible won't own up. The blame falls on Josh. The school is preparing a Passiontide play, and the story of Jesus' arrest and crucifixion stirs the consciences of those who have stolen from the sweet shop. They own up.

The school play ends with the Road to Emmaus where the risen Christ is recognised in the breaking of bread.